Dear Grandad

from you to me®

from you to me®

concept by Neil Coxon

Dear Grandad

from you to me®

This book is for your Grandfather's unique story.

It is for him to capture some of his life's key memories, experiences and feelings.

Ask him to complete it carefully and, if he wants to, add some photographs or images to personalise it more.

When it is finished and returned to you, this will be a record of his story . . . a story that you will treasure forever.

Dear

Here is a gift from me to you . . . for you to give to me.

When we are children we are always asking questions . . . well I now have some more for you.

Please could you answer them in the way that only you know how and then give the book back to me.

There might be a couple of questions that you prefer not to answer, so don't worry, just answer the others as well as you can . . . I won't mind.

People say that we all have at least one book in us, and this will be one of yours.

The story of you and me that I will treasure forever.

Thank you,

with love

Tell me about the **time** and **place** you were born . . .

What are your **earliest** memories?

I'd like to know about your parents . . . names, dates of birth and tell me some stories about them . . .

Tell me what you know about your Mother's parents and family . . .

Tell me what you know about your Father's parents and family . . .

Please detail what you know of our family tree …

What **interesting** information do you know about other people in our family?

Here's some space for you to add more about our family that will interest generations to come . . .

What do you remember about the place/s you lived when you were a child?

What were your favourite childhood toys or games?

What sort of pets did you have when you were young and what were their names?

What do you remember about your holidays as a child?

What did you do for entertainment when you were young?

What did you study at school and what were you best at?

Tell me about the things you **did** as a child that are **different** for today's children . . .

What did you want to do when you grew up?

What were your favourite hobbies when you were young?

Did you have an idol when you were young? Tell me who and why . . .

What was the first piece of music you bought?

What chores had to be done when you were young that aren't needed to be done today?

Describe any family traditions you had
or maybe still have

What age were you when you started work?
Tell me about the jobs you have had . . .

How did you meet my Grandmother?

What would you do for a **night-out** when you were **dating**?

Tell me about a **special** piece of **music** that you and my Grandmother had 'just for you' ...

Describe your **wedding** . . .

Choosing the names for your children can be really difficult . . . how did you decide?

I would love to know more about my parents
. . . what can you tell me?

Tell me what my **Mum** / **Dad** was **like** when they were younger . . .

How did you feel when you were told you were going to be a grandparent?

What did you think when you first saw me after
I was born?

Can you see any characteristics in me that come from other people in our family?

In what ways am I similar or different to my Mum / Dad?

Describe some of your favourite memories
of the times we have spent together . . .

Describe what you like about me . . .

Is there anything you would like to change about me?

Tell me about the friends you have had in your life . . .

What piece/s of music would you choose in your own favourite 'top 10'?

Tell me about the furthest place you have travelled to . . .

What are the happiest or greatest memories
of your life?

What are a few of your favourite things?

Describe your memory of some major world events that have happened in your lifetime . . .

Describe the greatest change that you have seen in your lifetime so far . . .

Do you think life today is better or worse than when you were young? How is it different?

Who or what has been the greatest influence on you?

If you were an animal . . . what type of animal would you be, and why?

If you won the Lottery . . . what would you do with the money?

What have you found most difficult in your life?

What is your **biggest regret** in your life?

Can you do anything about it **now**?

Tell me about the things that have made you happy or laugh . . .

With hindsight what would you do **differently**?

Describe something you still want to achieve in your life . . .

Tell me something you think I won't know about you . . .

What would you like your epitaph to say?

Given your experiences, what advice would you like to offer me?

And now your chance to tell me some other **personal stories** that you want to share . . .

These extra pages are for us to write any

questions, memories or answers that

may not have been covered elsewhere in the book . . .

And finally for the record . . .

what is your full name ?

what is your date of birth ?

what colour are your eyes ?

how tall are you ?

what blood group are you ?

what was the date when you completed this story for me ?

Dear

I will treasure this book, your memories and your advice forever.

I hope you enjoyed answering my questions.

Thank you so much for doing it and for writing your own book about you and me . . .

from you to me

Dear *Grandad*

from you to me®

First published in the UK by *from you to me*, August 2007
Copyright, *from you to me* limited 2007
Hackless House, Murhill, Bath, BA2 7FH
www.fromyoutome.com
E-mail: hello@fromyoutome.com

ISBN 978-1-907048-03-6

Cover design by so design consultants, Wick, Bristol, UK   www.so-design.co.uk
Printed and bound in the UK by CPI William Clowes, Beccles

This paper is manufactured from material sourced
from forests certified according to strict environmental,
social and economical standards.

If you think other questions should be included in future editions, please let
us know. And please share some of the interesting answers you receive with
us at the *from you to me* website to let other people read about these fascinating
insights . . .

If you liked the concept of this book, please tell your family and friends and
look out for others in the *from you to me* range:

> **Dear Mum, from you to me**
> **Dear Dad, from you to me**
> **Dear Grandma, from you to me**
> **Dear Sister, from you to me**
> **Dear Brother, from you to me**
> **Dear Friend, from you to me**
> **Cooking up Memories, from you to me**
> other relationships and memory journals coming soon . . .